DORA the EXPLORER

PHONI
READING PR

D0069967

Name That Friend

by Quinlan B. Lee

SCHOLASTIC INC.

New York   Toronto   London   Auckland   Sydney
Mexico City   New Delhi   Hong Kong   Buenos Aires

Do you think you
know my friends?
Let's play Name That
Friend and find out!
I will tell you the things
that each friend likes to do.
Then you see if you can
Name That Friend!
Let's play!

This friend has what
we need, in the rain
or in the sun.
If you need Sticky Tape
or rope, then you need
a friend like this one.
Name That Friend!

Yes!
That friend is Backpack.
She has the things that
we need.

Now see if you can
name this friend.
If you need to get
somewhere, he's a
good friend to know.
From the start to
the finish, he knows
the way to go.
Name That Friend!

That's it!
That friend is Map!
He always knows
the way to go.
The next one is a little
harder than the others.
Let's play!

These friends love to perform, and they play a merry tune. When it's time to shout, "WE DID IT!" you will see them very soon! Do you know these friends? Are they Tico and Boots?

No, it's the Fiesta Trio! There is one more friend left to name, and that will be the end of the game. Who comes on my adventures every day and helps me out along the way?

That's true. It's YOU!